# YOU ARE
## TOO MUCH,

# CHARLIE BROWN

Selected Cartoons From

## BUT WE LOVE YOU, CHARLIE BROWN
### Vol. II

by Charles M. Schulz

A FAWCETT CREST BOOK
FAWCETT PUBLICATIONS, INC., GREENWICH, CONN.

# THE PEANUTS GALLERY

## includes:

HERE COMES CHARLIE BROWN     M2580
> (selected cartoons from *Good Ol' Charlie Brown,* Vol. 2)

CHARLIE BROWN AND SNOOPY     M2581
> (selected cartoons from *As You Like It, Charlie Brown,* Vol. 1)

HERE'S TO YOU, CHARLIE BROWN     M2582
> (selected cartoons from *You Can't Win, Charlie Brown,* Vol. 1)

THE WONDERFUL WORLD OF PEANUTS     M2583
> (selected cartoons from *More Peanuts,* Vol. 1)

*Only 95 Cents Each Wherever Paperbacks Are Sold*

YOU ARE TOO MUCH, CHARLIE BROWN

This book, prepared especially for Fawcett Publications, Inc., comprises the second half of BUT WE LOVE YOU, CHARLIE BROWN, and is reprinted by arrangement with Holt, Rinehart and Winston, Inc.

PRIDE OF OWNERSHIP...

SCHULZ

"PIG-PEN" IS THE ONLY PERSON I KNOW WHO CAN GET DIRTY WALKING IN A SNOWSTORM!